A Gift of Grace

by Noelle Sellers

A love story

agiftofgrace1@gmail.com

50 Percent of the profits of this book will be donated equally to:

The Salvation Army

salvationarmyusa.org

and

Hope Global Initiative

hopegi.org

This book is dedicated to my three children

I love you all

Forward

I am certainly not an eloquent writer, and not a famous author. This book began as a small seed, planted years ago, long before I ever dreamed of writing. What would happen if you sat down and wrote a love story? What would yours look like? When my messy life got in the way, that only made the story turn out better; the book became my little garden that I took care of. It started out as my journal years ago. At first it was something no one would ever want to read. As God changed my life, I went back and changed the story. It grew and blossomed until the day that it was ready. Beautiful flowers are meant to be shared. Even if I was once nothing but a small bud, God took the time to cultivate me. He planted me long before I knew what he would do. It's not every day that you fall in love with your best friend and he ends up saving your life. Isn't that how all the best stories end? His name is the sweetest one I know. All along he had the patience to let my little garden grow.

Special thanks goes out to all the people in my life who helped me turn my huge run on sentence into a book. To Calysta Anderson, Bethany Sellers, and Kristin Griffin, thank you for your help in editing. Evangeline Sellers, thank you for your beautiful artwork.

Contents

Chapter One: Grace's Garden

Imagine a butterfly floating through the air with colors as vivid as stained glass windows. It's a miraculous creature that begins life as a tiny egg, an egg as small as a mustard seed. Each step along the journey is orchestrated by divine design, but it's journey didn't start out this way! The amazing transformation process from caterpillar to butterfly serves a purpose. With wings like soft lemon meringue, it's so delicate that its gracefulness can be *felt*. In the end, the butterfly emerges to be beautiful in just the right time!

Nature has a way of healing the soul. The process of my own personal healing began as a tiny seed inside me, growing until my heart would one day again be in full bloom. Just like a flower that bursts forth after the dead of winter, I felt my heart being restored after an excruciating trial in my life. All the little pieces that needed to be put back together were ready to be assembled. This healing didn't come from my own strength but from a very unexpected source.

My journey began when I encountered a garden near my home when I was searching for a new place to be outdoors.

The garden wasn't far from my house, out in the middle
nowhere. I was living close to a treasure all this time witho
knowing it. In front of the entrance, there was a beauti
wooden sign that was so small it might have been misse
"Grace's Garden," it read in ornate script. I turned the whe
of my car into the drive and came to a stop to peer at the sig
It appeared to be hand-carved and very old. Each letter w
perfectly chiseled and sanded with great care. Someone h
nailed a little rider to the top that read, "VOLUNTEEI
NEEDED."

The moment my feet started crunching on the grav
pathways, I fell in love with the peaceful atmosphe
Intoxicating lavender drifted up to my nose, and I noticed t
faint strumming of wings. My eyes delighted in the differe
varieties of planted flowers that burst from the earth in colo
of the sunset like sprays of fireworks. There were millions
them, stretching over rolling hills as far as the eye could see

A golden glow washed through the fragments of the tr
limbs and cast itself down to the ferns that blanketed the u
sculpted beds. Giant boulders burst from the landscape he
and there.

A sense of peace washed over me as I inhaled the richness of the earth. It ended up becoming my sanctuary.

In the middle of the garden, there was a mysterious inner island, forming an inner court. It was surrounded by a bubbling spring that created a mote around it. The water was crystal clear and trickled along its rocky bed. In its center, it contained nothing more than a very large tree stump.

It was never crowded. Few people strolled the paths, and there was a Gardener, who was always tending to the plants. He was an older man, but walked with a strong, sure step. His hair was white, thick and unkept. He had a lengthy, white beard and crinkled brown skin that suggested he had been in the sun for many years. His clothes were worn and tattered, and he had an ease about him that seemed extremely familiar. He handled his tools with capable hands that were never in a hurry.

Healing is like walking through a garden over time. Each day was the gradual rebirthing of fragments that needed to be replanted and take root in a new beginning.

The process hurt at times, with new roots breaking free and reaching out where there hadn't been any before.

I had to learn to be patient with the process, just li
pruning helps a plant to grow and thrive.

I had two daughters and a son who were very loved. N
middle daughter ended up staying with her dad instead
with me during our divorce. Through circumstances beyo
my control, I didn't see her very much, and it began to sink
that I wouldn't have much of a relationship with her at all
had a wonderful, supportive family who were there for
and I was very thankful for them. However, I felt tota
helpless and out of control. I didn't know what to do abc
the loss of my daughter, so I sank to my knees by my bo
crying out in desperation.

Loss comes to everyone on earth at some point in time.
will all eventually lose someone we love to the grip of dea
Then comes the pain, and the grieving process.

But what happens when your child is still alive? S
continues life without me. I feel that I've been cut out of it,
if she has died. I call it "a living death".

When a loved one dies, there is closure at some point
time because you no longer imagine a life with them. There
no closure when the loved one remains.

My baby girl lives fifteen minutes down the road from me, and her memories are fading from my mind as if she no longer existed. She is going on through the years without me; she is picking out her prom dress, driving a car for the first time, and graduating high school. All the moments that I would have experienced with her are being cut out of my heart like pages that are slowly ripped out of the beautifully written novel of our lives. I watched other people enjoy precious moments like these with their own children, while I imagined it happening in my own mind. Death doesn't allow memories to go on; it was cruel for my daughter to remain alive, yet ripped away from my life. *I felt cheated out of her love.*

I had a desperate fear of losing my other children. I grasped onto them, clinging to intimacy. I poured all my love and attention into them because I didn't want to lose them as well. I was worried that I wasn't a good enough mother; that I would never be enough for them. I lived in a prison of regret and anxiety, and I drank at night to numb my feelings. I made terrible decisions and gave in to my carnal desires. I went through the motions around the people who knew me, and talking about it didn't help.

The hole in my heart was so deep, that I felt like I wou[l]
be destined to die without real love. Nothing filled the hu[g]
black void in my heart.

I never imagined that I would find love again in [a]
unexpected place. I didn't realize that eventually I wou[l]
meet my best friend, who would put all those ripped pag[e]
from the novel of our lives back together. In my innermo[s]
heart I deeply desired for him to restore all the relationshi[p]
in my life, but we are all sinners. There is no distinctic[n]
between us all. I thought I was drowning, but I wasn't. [H]
had to break me, taking away everything that I placed abo[v]
him, so that he could lead me across dry ground. *Instead, [H]
restored me to himself.*

Chapter Two: The Greenhouse

In a butterfly's life, the complete metamorphosis involves four miraculous stages. These are the egg, larva, pupa, (chrysalis) and adult butterfly. A butterfly begins life as an intricate egg. If you peer close enough to the egg, you can see the tiny caterpillar growing inside of it. This humble egg is only the start of the stunning masterpiece that is revealed at the end. Each detail of this creature comes together like a puzzle knit in the belly of the chrysalis. God has a plan from the beginning!

There is something about the regeneration of nature that is very healing for the soul. I started going to Grace's Garden consistently, and I became familiar with the squishy sound the moss made under my feet.

I was strolling through the acres of the grounds one day and took a turn down a path I had never been down before.

As I was walking along I noticed that some of the flowers along the path had been up-rooted with a little bit of dirt littering the path. I stopped to wonder about this, then kept going.

There was a glimmer peeking through the foliage up ahead and I became very curious. When I came upon the light, I realized it was an old greenhouse and was made entirely of green glass.

Its panels sparkled and gave off a verdant glow. I moved a little closer and noticed a front door with a handle and no lock. My eyes scanned all around the door, and on the upper left side was a small wooden sign that read, "Lamb of God." I looked around to see if anyone was there, but it looked deserted. Feeling curious, I slowly opened the door and poked my head inside. The first thing that I noticed was the feeling of fluttering wings across my face! I shut my eyes in surprise, then again and again more wings caressed my features like the whisper of feathers.

I swiftly moved inside and shut the door behind me, my eyes adjusting to the emerald glow that radiated within. What I saw took my breath away.

The glass room was larger than it seemed from the outside and it was filled with lush foliage that crawled up the sides fanning to the ceiling. Sinewy vines clung to the heavy glass walls. Myriads of pure snow white daisies dotted the interior floor, raising their faces toward the light above.

Countless butterflies drifted through the air in so many colors, like the kaleidoscope of a crayon box. Trailing behind each one through the air was a beautiful stream of light that resembled a flame. The sun crept powerfully through the glass roof and dripped inside with golden fingers.

My jaw dropped open slightly as I took it all in, and I knew I had entered a sacred place. I gazed around in astonishment at the artistry that was flourishing in that greenhouse on just an ordinary day. The spun cocoon of a chrysalis caught my eye as it hung from a delicately swaying leaf. *I felt like I had entered heaven's jewelry box.*

Just then, a back door hidden from behind a creeping vine opened, and the Gardener slipped through the door. He was wearing old overalls that displayed a few holes, and a tattered cloak. His white hair was unruly and wild.

He looked straight into my eyes with a smile, his eyes lit up with kindness and warmth, and he said my name out loud. The sound of it shocked me, rolling off his lips as he moved forward toward the blossoms in the center of the room where I was standing. *How does he know my name?* I thought. His voice reverberated off the glass walls of the greenhouse, strong and permeating like peals of thunder.

He came closer to me, and the air became heavy, pressing on my body. The butterflies rose higher in the room as his footsteps reached the daisies. He raised his right hand into the air and a single butterfly landed delicately on his finger.

"Let them come to me…" he said, the words tumbling out of his mouth and vibrating off the glass. The butterflies rose in unison, and like the notes of a dazzling song, each one landed on him until he was covered in a sea of trembling colors.

I was speechless, as he stood there swathed from head to foot in vivid butterflies. I had never seen anything like this before!

Then, as quickly as they came, the butterflies bolted in flight, and with blazes of light trailing behind them, they landed on the daisies. They softly perched one on each flower, as delicate as angels.

The Gardener reached his hand out over the butterflies with his eyes tightly shut, and he prayed for them. The words came out of his mouth in a whisper that I could comprehend.

"What are these?" I asked him.

He looked over at me with a knowing smile.

"The Spirits of Wisdom," he replied. "The helpers, my advocates that I am sending to all mankind. Sometimes grace comes from an unexpected place."

I gazed in wonder at the sight. "*What do I say?*" I thought.

He seemed to know what I was thinking, and looked over at me in merriment.

"Would you like a bite to eat?" he asked. "I would love something," I said as a smile crept across my face.

"I have a little place out back and some bread warming by a fire," he said as he motioned to the back door where he had entered.

I followed him through the back door and into the yard of the greenhouse where there was a little clearing. In it, a one-man canvas tent had been carefully pitched with ropes, and in front of it was a campfire. There was a shelf on a nearby tree with a cup and plate, and some odds and ends used as toiletries. A saw horse with carving tools and chisels stood near the tree. Wood shavings littered the ground below. A makeshift wooden bench made of logs had been placed by the fire. Its simplicity was inviting. *This must be his home,* I thought to myself.

The smell of fresh bread was in the air, along with the aroma of burning wood from the fire. There was a small flame going under the kindling, and a loaf pan off to the side keeping warm.

"You are welcome to sit," said the Gardener. I brightened at his invitation and joined him on the wooden bench.

Then I looked around at his humble surroundings and asked, "Do you live here in this tent?"

He reached out for the loaf of bread. "Yes, I do. But soon will have a new home forever." I watched him with curiosity, his presence making me very aware.

There was something about him that was so trustworthy and uplifting. He reached out in an easy-going manner and took the loaf of bread. The inside was fluffy with a crusty amber top. I watched his hands easily tear off a piece, and he handed it to me, saying, "Eat this, and at the right time, you will remember me."

I reached out for the morsel of bread, and its steam wafted toward me. A faint bouquet of sweetness tempered with ear' filled my senses.

He watched me closely as I put it in my mouth, and my eyes grew wide with pleasure. The bread melted like spun sugar instantly on my tongue.

"This is glorious!" I murmured with a mouth half full. The Gardener tossed his white hair back and let out a throaty laugh that came from deep within. "How could I forget something like this?" I continued in amazement as I swallowed.

I took another bite and kept chewing when out of the corner of my eye, I saw a glimpse of a red shadow off to the side. I jerked my head around to pinpoint where it was coming from, and saw a rustling in a thicket close by.

I stared at the tall grass, my breathing becoming more shallow with trepidation. The reeds parted, and a red fox slunk out from within them and sauntered right over to us.

I exhaled in relief at the sight of the harmless fox. It was unusually large, with a shiny, orange-red coat, and a pompous white tipped tail. It looked me full in the eyes while its fluffy tail whipped slowly back and forth.

The fox opened his mouth to speak, and I stared at him in surprise. "Hope you're enjoying the garden," he said slyly.

His voice was gravelly and low, and something about him was foreboding.

"I've been watching the light in the greenhouse, and wondering what you are doing in there, Mr. Lamb," he remarked. He came a little closer, his body silent and slinky. The Gardener serenely watched every move and didn't take his eyes off him. "I have a goal," he replied.

The fox nudged a small rock that was lying on the ground with his front paws and moved it towards the Gardener with his slimy black nose until it laid at his feet.

"Since apparently you are able to do anything in this garden, then turn this rock into bread for me, so I don't go hungry," he said to the Gardener, with twitching whiskers. His eyes were huge and innocent, and he stared directly at him with a haughty challenge. I didn't dare say anything. I was astonished at the fox's boldness and looked from the rock back to the delicious bread in my hand.

The Gardener didn't bat an eye, and calmly picked up a sturdy stick and began to poke at the fire.

"My gifts give life and joy to all who believe," he said.

With this he gave a wink in the fox's direction and the fox's face slowly changed with rage. "And so do my words," the Gardener added with finality.

The scarlet hair on the fox's back and tail bristled back and forth. Finally, he stood up on his haunches, turned, and stalked off into the garden. In the distance, I could hear the distinct crowing of a rooster.

"What was that all about?" I asked, looking at the Gardener with curiosity.

"The fox's time here is limited," he said, "but he denies it."

I looked in surprise at the place where the fox had stalked off into the thicket, and wondered at how an animal could talk!

"He won't go hungry?" I asked as I looked after him.

"No," the Gardener replied. "He eats grass like an ox. And if you see him again you can tell that fox that I will reach my goal."

The sun was beginning to set, so I thanked the Gardener for the bread, a delicacy I would never forget, and the experience watching him in the greenhouse with the butterflies. He took me into his arms for a warm hug, and I went home that day thinking about what had happened.

Chapter Three: I Catch Every Tear

Butterfly larvae are what we call caterpillars. Caterpillars don't stay in this stage for very long. When the egg hatches, the caterpillar will begin working by eating the leaf it was born on. A mother butterfly needs to lay her eggs on a compatible leaf, because the larva can't travel to a new plant. When caterpillars start eating, they instantly start growing and expanding. Their exoskeleton doesn't stretch, so they shed their skin several times. The butterfly works hard and does everything with a purpose. Before the butterfly is reborn and free, total transformation must happen. Development can be difficult and chaotic, but the end goal is to be transformed into the most beautiful canvas, and it's worth the wait!

Each day in my life was like the unfolding of a new beginning. Little by little, the process was like planting a garden and watching it grow.

I believed in the healing of a broken heart, but I didn't know how to give up control of my life, because I honestly only trusted myself. I didn't know how to trust in God because I felt like he wasn't there for me.

This was the kind of thing I didn't tell anyone, because I didn't want to be judged. Soon he would show me that true friendship is unconditional, and what he saw in me is better than what others think about me.

Over the summer, Grace's Garden transformed and regenerated itself, taking my breath away.

The flowers stretched over the rolling hills as far as my eye could see in golds, crimson, and violet. Bird song wobbled through summer breezes with notes like refreshing mint lemonade.

One particular day, I came up a path and spied the Gardener. I climbed up a small boulder to watch him work. He finished with a rake and picked up some flowers. He drove his shovel into the soft earth and placed a zinnia into the hole with such deliberate care that I was transfixed by the tenderness of his actions.

He tucked the plant in and squished the folds of dirt around the roots until the plant stood straight to attention. I watched as one tiny petal from the flower detached from the stalk and fell.

His strong arm lanced out with lightning speed and caught the petal before it could hit the ground!

He carefully tucked it in one of the pockets of his frayed shirt. Then, he reached into another pocket and took out a small, worn leather journal and scribbled something in it. Then, he replaced the journal in his pocket.

He continued planting, contented to leave a weed here and there amongst the carefully placed flowers.

When he was finished, he slowly raised his ancient body in one long motion, and stood to look in satisfaction at the bed he had made. He smiled at it warmly, like a father smiles at his child.

I quickly slid off the boulder and walked over to him. He turned toward me, and as I was coming said my name out loud before I reached him. "Hey there!" I said brightly as I reached his side. *How does he know me?* I thought.

He smiled at me and his face lit up like the sun, toughened from myriads of lines that carved deep grooves into his skin. "What did you write in the book?" I asked him. He gave a little pat to the pocket where he had tucked the petal.

"I catch every tear. Every one," he replied, "and then I take note of them." I stood before him in shock. The notes of his voice crashed into my ears.

"Every single one?" I managed to squeak out.

"Of course," he said. The orbs of his eyes were deep and warm, like a fire on a chilly winter's night. His gaze held mine as it seemed to pierce through my skin down to my bones, reaching to search the innermost parts of my heart.

I stood there frozen in time, unafraid as he probed. almost felt like flying...

It was then that I realized he already knew me, and had known me since before I was born. When he saw the moment that I became aware of this, a slow smile crept across his face as he gently let go of my heart. In my limited capacity, thought he was searching for something, but he didn't need to. There was nothing about me he didn't already see.

He was gently reminding me that he was in control, and stood there completely humbled. He didn't need a testimony about mankind, for he knew what was in each person.

His eyes unlocked with mine, and he turned on his heel sure of himself and offering no further explanation.

The air around us was thick and heavy, pressing on me like two ton bricks. As he walked away, the weight subsided little. I drove home in silence that day, wondering about the little petals and how valuable they were to the Gardener.

I thought about how intimately he knew me, and I felt very precious to him. I felt myself begin to heal as I let him into my heart and took down the walls. Healing is a healthy process, just like the caterpillar takes the time to regenerate, emerging to be a beautiful masterpiece. This involved letting God take the time to cultivate and nourish every little part in the garden of my heart.

I decided right then and there that I was a failure only in my own eyes, not in God's. I didn't want to hold on to bitterness and unforgiveness anymore. Some of the tears I cried were becoming strokes to my ego and keeping me from healing. I wanted to think about how to focus on serving others instead of feeling sorry for myself.

I stayed in close relationship with family who helped me learn to recognize when I was suppressing my emotions. I had to rewire my brain to react to stress instead of avoiding it. This allowed me to feel joy as well as the sorrow I was going through.

I talked to a counselor and people who were close to me. As the pit of depression slowly started to lift, I stopped some bad habits.

I had to learn to process my feelings instead of bottling them up. Drinking at night lost its comfort for me, and I gave it up.

I was going through uncharted territory, so I knew I couldn't stay in the state that I was in. I started taking the time to focus on healing, but ultimately, it was going to take more than the strength that I was able to give.

I began painting like I used to do years ago, and brush strokes flowed on canvas again. Journaling and writing became my healthy escape and nature was like time out for my soul.

When I was a little girl, I talked to God face to face like a best friend. I humbled myself again like a small child and told him that I desperately needed him. All of us have become like one who is unclean, and all our righteous acts are like filthy rags; we all shrivel up like a leaf, and like the wind, our sin sweep us away. *I asked him to restore my heart.*

Chapter Four: A Perfect Single Daisy

As soon as a caterpillar reaches its full body weight, it envelops itself in a silky chrysalis. From the outside, it looks as if the caterpillar may just be resting, but inside is where the real action is. This process is better than a five star movie! The caterpillar is undergoing an amazing transformation called metamorphosis, where our hero is being regenerated behind the scenes! Even the limbs and tissues have all been changed by the time the butterfly is complete. The butterflies body parts melt into a rich liquid and break down in order to form a completely new body. In the same way that a super hero transforms from inside a phone booth, the butterfly will burst out a brand new creature! God in his wisdom doesn't allow the butterfly to skip the growing process.

With each season that changed the landscape in Grace's Garden, the evidence of a creator weaved itself through every vein of every leaf.

The Gardener was there, going up and down the paths with ease, carefully planting and tending to the grounds. He seemed to have a lot of work to accomplish…

I was curious about the inner court, so I started looking for a way so I could pass over the spring to get to it, but I didn't see one. As I was walking along I spotted a small sign near the water.

The sign was very old and made of beautifully hand carved wood, with wild brush growing at its base. It was perched on a firm stake that had been driven into the ground. In capital letters it spelled out "LIFE." I looked across at the spring, and saw that the water was steadily rising. Instead of a trickle, was now ankle deep. The stump that was in the middle had sprouted green shoots that were growing in every direction. A few leaves were budding from the shoots as it was beginning to grow again!

I was observing the stump and when I turned to go, nearly collided with the fox! I scrambled to catch myself and narrowly missed stepping on his tail.

"Well, hello again," he purred, unaffected by our run-in.

I looked around in a bit of a panic for the Gardener but didn't see him, so I straightened my back and bravely looked the fox full in the face.

"Oh, hey," I said as I swept a little dust off my clothes. "Where have you been?" The fox laid a sack at his feet that he was carrying, and stood straight up on his hind legs like a man.

"From roaming throughout the earth, going back and forth on it," he replied. "I take some of the flowers along the path when I can. Some have no root, and some get choked, so I rip them up."

"You're an idiot," I replied. "The Gardener will always plant more!"

He half-closed his eyes, his back straight and tall.

"You know, all authority in this garden has been given to me," he said slyly. He waited and looked down at one paw as if bored with the thought. I stared at him. Then he slowly looked up and his eyes met mine with a piercing glare. I could see the whites that surrounded his hazel-green irises, and his white whiskers twitched. I shuddered a little inside as his eyes locked onto mine, and I detected a deep blackness that felt like drowning.

"I can give this garden to anyone I want to. That old man who tries to run things here needs to retire. He's past his time, and even worse, he doesn't require anything for admission!"

The fox spat on the ground and I quickly moved my feet out of his way. I could see the anger building inside him although he was trying very hard to hold himself together.

"There's no cost to get in here and that shouldn't be! There isn't enough room for everyone!" he hissed.

He began pacing up and down the path in indignation. "He never stops planting those flowers!" he practically screamed. "There's millions of them here, but day and night, he just doesn't stop!" He stopped pacing, and paused to compose himself. His eyes zeroed into mine and darted to and fro in desperation. I snickered to myself as I realized that he was desperate for answers. I looked around at the expanse of the garden, at the multitude of colors that wound like ribbons throughout the hills as far as the eye could see. For a minute, the thought of owning such a beautiful sanctuary entered my head and filled my mind with pleasurable daydreams.

He leaned in a little closer, and I could smell his pungent breath. "You and I could own Grace's Garden together," he said.

"I'll charge a hefty admission fee for everyone, and they will have to do certain things in order to get in. It can't be free!"

The distinct sound of a rooster started a throaty crowing in the distance, and my mind instantly snapped back to reality.

I remembered seeing the "VOLUNTEERS NEEDED" sign at the front entrance to the garden, and I thought about what the Gardener would say if he were standing there right now.

"I'd rather serve here than own the place," I said to the fox firmly. "And I think the Gardener is doing a wonderful job tending to this garden!" I stomped off toward the exit to go home. Then, I turned on my heel and glared at the fox. "Oh, and he said to tell you that he will accomplish his goal!" I heard the fox suck in a breath of disgust as I walked away.

I knew there was something about him I didn't trust, and I wanted to get away from him as quickly as possible.

I could feel his haughty eyes piercing the back of my shirt as I moved toward the exit, and I was determined to have nothing more to do with him.

Time was going by, and like the metamorphosis of the caterpillar, I was changing inside. A key opened my heart and the door slowly swung open.

I began to believe that God could really lift me away from the filthy, dirty parts that no one saw that had been broken and shattered. I was including him in my daily conversations and feeling his presence.

He had planted me before I ever believed in myself. He nurtured me in the palm of his hand, and he saw the beauty of the flower that I was all along.

All I had to do was see myself through his lens. All my life I had limited him, confining him to a building within four walls, but I didn't find him there.

I didn't experience him by following rules or what mankind says I should do. He was in the dust as I moved about the grounds of my favorite garden, and in the warmth of the sun as it washed over me.

Who has measured the waters in the hollow of his hand, or with the breadth of his hand marked off the heavens? Who has held the dust of the earth in a basket, or weighed the mountains on the scales and the hills in a balance?

I knew I was a sinner, and couldn't save myself by my own strength. I believed in Jesus as the son of God who died for me on the cross, paying the penalty for me. I believed him and repented, and he washed me white as snow.

After I took personal responsibility for my sins and my actions, my relationship with him grew as I got to know him intimately. He cultivated the little garden within my heart and we became best friends.

I thought about my middle daughter, and our lack of relationship. I had to let go in order to let God heal that part of me. I realized that he would take care of her even if I wasn't involved in her life for now, and it was more important that she was happy and healthy.

Even though I ended up seeing her about twice over the next few years, I continued to contact her anyway. I knew it was important to stay strong and continue to reach out to her.

Over time, I could talk about her to others without being upset. I accepted the fact that she might be ok living her life without me, because he will take care of her.

My end goal became to lead her towards him by my actions, because her salvation was more important than the fact that I needed to restore a relationship with her at any cost.

She was always invited to family holidays, and one year she agreed to come to Thanksgiving. My large family decided to meet at my parents house.

It was ideal weather outside, so we set up tables and chairs in the yard and driveway to sit and eat. When my daughter arrived, I could hear my own heartbeat in my head. I thought about how much courage it must have taken for her come that day!

As we talked a little, I could tell she felt awkward, and my heart went out to her. So much time had gone by since the last time I saw her that I didn't recognize her! I looked into my own daughter's face like she was a total stranger, and the weight of this realization hit me like a ton of bricks.

Her voice sounded different because she was becoming woman.

The features on her face were different than when she was younger. She laughed with confidence and spoke about her school and friends, and I hung onto every word, curious about her new life. She had changed over time like a hidden beauty that had emerged from out of a hiding place. I was so proud of the young lady she had become!

Not wanting to overwhelm her, I asked general questions about her life. It had been so long that I had been involved her life that I felt like I was interviewing a long lost friend.

When I looked deep into her eyes, I knew she was still the same little girl that I had mothered and raised...

As time went on, healing crept in like a blossoming tree. The seed was planted long before I ever believed life could change. Then one day, my best friend would sign his name on my heart...

Clouds swept through the sky like cotton balls and the air was a little cooler. I strolled confidently up and down the familiar paths of Grace's Garden. Thousands of flowers were blooming and their fragrance drifted through the air.

Bees scampered over the flowers like picnickers looking for the perfect spot to lay their blankets in the sun.

When I walked past the inner court, I looked over at the spring and noticed that the stump had now grown into a promising tree, about five feet tall.

Its leaves were bountiful, spilling off the branches in the hundreds, with bright new green shoots emerging to add to its fullness.

Its trunk was rugged, and I could tell it was going to be a very large tree. I stopped to look at it for a minute, then kept walking until I sat down in the shade on a ledge of a koi pond.

I thought about the journey my life had taken and how healing was happening. I heard strong steps come crunching up the gravel path and knew it was the Gardener. I brightened when I saw his face, and when he got closer to me, the air closed in and the familiar pressure of his presence settled on me, humbling me to my inner core.

This time, he sat right beside me in the pleasant breeze and was silent for a few minutes. Finally, he spoke.

"Who do you say I am?" I didn't have to think about his question because I already knew the answer.

"You are the Lamb of God, who takes away the sins of the world." I answered, looking straight into his eyes.

"What you say is right," he replied.

"I have a gift for you, a priceless gift," he said warmly, as he peered into my face with a smile. I wondered what it could be, and glanced down at his empty hands. I noticed surprise that puncture wounds were carved deep through the flesh on each of his wrists, as if he had been pierced all the way through with some kind of sharp object. I looked back into his face and he was frozen with anticipation, his eyes wide around the map that carved lines in his cheeks. "I love you," he said softly.

The color drained from my face as his words crashed into the little fleshy parts of my ears. "*Why me?*" I wondered to myself in surprise. He smiled tenderly. "Well, there is only one you!" he said.

Then, he reached out with his hand to withdraw a single daisy laying beside him.

"*It's the Spirit of Wisdom,*" he said.

My mouth dropped open at the sight of the simple gift, and I slowly reached out to accept it from him. The moment that my skin touched the snow white petals, a tingly feeling began to build inside of me.

It started as a small seed, growing in strength until my entire body was violently buzzing with the sensation of a thousand ants!

My fingers grasped the daisy as the Gardener sat back and watched me with a huge, satisfied grin. The tingly feeling radiated throughout my body as I held the flower. I let go of the daisy in shock and watched it fall into my lap, then disappear. The tingles continued to move through me in a miraculous way. "Now a part of me is in you, and I will always be with you. I've reached my goal, my covenant that is poured out for many," he said, his smile radiating upon me.

As the feeling permeated my body, I looked up into his crinkled eyes that were brimming over with love. He was crying.

Chapter Five: The Tree of Life

Finally, when the caterpillar has done all of its changing inside the chrysalis, a newly developed butterfly breaks free! When it first comes out, its wings are tender and folded against its body. As the butterfly rests, it gently flaps its wings in order to pump life into the folded wings stretching them out to be functional. Usually within several hours, the butterfly will master flying! When it finally finds a suitable bloom to land on, it folds its wings neatly upward like painted silk to extract the sweet nectar. Now vital and strong, its course is set, and its wings are determined. Once only a tiny egg, the butterfly has now become beautiful in the right time.

One morning the sun was just rising over the treetops across the street from my home. As I stretched and looked out the window, I sucked in a breath of joy when I saw the wonders that were painted in the sky.

Everything was different now, and many of the hardened parts of my heart had melted away. *I had been given a new heart.*

Life wasn't perfect but I wasn't living in prison anymore. felt completely changed from the inside out. I felt like caged bird that had been set free!

I wasn't in control anymore, which meant God was. I wa finally telling him that I trusted him. I realized that purpose not the action I take, but the unique strength he planted withi me. He loved me for who I was before I ever loved hin Maybe a weed is really a flower that refuses to let his love i Now that he was blooming in my heart, I wanted to rest in h shade forever.

The sun dripped down through the sky, warming my ha as I marched into Grace's Garden. I was determined to fir out how I could reach the tree called "LIFE" in the inn court.

I didn't take the usual detours, but headed straight to tl middle, where the spring and tree were located. It was earl and a blanket of dew was still on the ground.

The Gardener was watering bulbs he had just planted ne the spring. I was as silent as a mouse as I crept up behi him, but he somehow knew I was coming and turned off t hose.

I smiled and moved forward, happy to see him again.

His wrinkled, time worn face lit up to greet me as he turned around. He called me by my name like he did before, his voice resonating and strong.

I stopped right in front of him this time, putting my hands in my pockets, almost at a loss for words now that I was standing before him.

Glancing at the tree that was growing steadily taller over us, I said, "I've been everywhere in the garden except for here in the middle where the tree is, and I can't find a way in! Can you help me?" His lips widened into a warm smile.

"I thought you would never ask!" he laughed. He laid the hose on the ground and smiled at the Tree of Life that was steadily growing in splendor. "I own this garden," he said firmly. I let out a nervous laugh. "Oh, I didn't know that! The fox told me that it had been given to him, and I didn't know what he was talking about," I said. He stroked his beard in amusement.

"The garden has a true owner. I AM HE," he said with final authority. "All authority in heaven and on earth has been given to me. Whoever believes in me shall not perish but have eternal life.

I'm a carpenter, and I come from a small town. This tree i[s] for the whole world, and I tend to it. I have a lot of leaves, s[o] many to care for!

Everyone will rest in its shade. All it takes is a littl[e] grace," he said with a knowing smile.

With a slow movement, he bent down to sit on a benc[h] nearby. Stretching out his legs, he gazed up at the growin[g] expanse of foliage above us.

The wind delicately drifted through the boughs and stood in its quiet beauty. "There is a spring that has to b[e] crossed in order to reach the tree," he continued.

I looked over at the crystal clear water and peered dow[n] into the spring. It was now knee deep. The waters we[re] rushing, and it was getting dangerous to cross it alone.

There was a rustling sound, and suddenly the wind shift[ed] in the opposite direction. From behind a neighboring group [of] cat tails, the fox emerged, with his head hung low to t[he] ground. He padded slowly forward until he stood straig[ht] between me and the Gardener. My back stiffened at the sig[ht] of him. He didn't say anything, but stared into my eyes.

He turned up his snout into the air and let out a faint snort. He kept staring blankly at me until I was uncomfortable with his gaze, so I turned back to the Gardener.

"The spring is beautiful," I said. "Does it have a name?"

"The Jordan," he said, as he glanced at the fox, who was immediately repulsed.

"There will come a day when I will help the people cross and reach the Tree of Life." My eyes grew wide in surprise.

"When will this be?" I stammered.

"When the tree is fully grown," he replied. "The tree has experienced a hardening in part until the full number of leaves come in. My Father, who has given them to me, is greater than all; no one can snatch them out of my fathers hand. I and the Father are one."

I let out the breath of air I didn't know I was holding in. I looked at the fox who broke my gaze and looked sheepishly at an ant crawling in front of him. "Make no mistake, this is my tree, and it will shelter the whole world, just as I intend." commanded the Gardener. My gaze shifted from his face to the fox's. The wind blew the Gardener's gangly white hair across his forehead. His visage was ancient and regal like a kings.

Then I looked at the fox, who contorted with uncontrollable anger. He reached out with his paw and crushed the ant that was scurrying along in front of him. swallowed hard.

With a tiny voice, I said, "So when that time comes, all the people will cross together?" The Gardener smiled so widely that the warmth penetrated my skin.

"Yes!" he exclaimed with a voice that boomed like thunder.

"When the people cross, it will be a great day of celebration!"

I was speechless after he said this, and the fox started sulking and playing with the ant's lifeless body with the tip of his claw.

Then the fox stood up as tall and straight as he could manage, emphatically clearing his throat. "You know, Mr Lamb, if you really are the true owner of this garden, why don't you prove it to her? Climb to the top of the Tree of Life and throw yourself down. Your precious angels, the butterflies, will hear you fall and come lift you up with their wings." I stared at the fox in disbelief.

A moment of dead silence passed. The fox hung his head a little bit, and a mocking sadness came over his face. "That is…" he said, "If you ARE who you say you are."

My head whipped around to look at the Gardener who was observing the tree calmly. He stood there for so many seconds that I didn't think he was going to answer. The fox started to chuckle under his breath and slowly he shook his head. The reeds close by parted and a stately rooster strutted out into the clearing. Its black, blood red, and carrot colored feathers rustled. Stopping just before us, it cocked its head to the side to look at us with a beady eye.

The tension in the air was thick as the rooster cleared its throat and prepared to let out a hearty crow. Beads of sweat formed on my forehead.

Then, the Gardener looked over at me with steady features, his eyes giving me a knowing gleam. He reached into the pocket of his torn shirt and took out his little journal.

The rooster drew his head back preparing to let out a blast, and the fox shifted uneasily from one foot to the other. The Gardener opened the worn pages of his journal and cupped his hand over the book so no one could see what he quickly read.

The fox was visibly agitated as he replaced the journal back into his pocket and calmly gave us all the tiniest smile. "Don't tempt me," he said, his voice piercing the air.

The rooster had been holding his breath and his eyes popped in surprise! Instead of a crow, he quickly subdued himself and what came out was a hiccup instead. Embarrassed, he cocked his tail feathers and flounced off towards the thicket.

The Gardener shifted his gaze over to the fox. "GET BEHIND ME SATAN!" he said, the tempo of his voice so strong that all the leaves above us trembled and shook. The fox cowered backwards, slinking down to the ground.

Then, without batting an eye, the Gardener turned 'around with poise and reached for the water hose to start watering the bulbs just as he was before. As I watched him work, I felt a strong urge to be involved in the process. "Can I help you with that?" I asked him.

He turned toward me and I could see his chest swell with pride. "I do need volunteers!" he said kindly.

I reached out to take the hose from him and felt the tingly sensation permeate downwards through my body as I watered each bulb.

As I watched the droplets fall softly on the ground, I realized that we love because he first loved us...

Hugging the Gardener, I said goodby and left that day with a hopeful heart. I knew everything would be okay, because I fully trusted in him to keep his word and knew he was in control. I don't think I had ever seen the fox look so defeated! I laughed about it all the way home.

Eventually, the seasons changed once more, and the air became brisk, piercing through the strands of my hair like ice as I hurried down the street to the neighborhood coffee shop. Cold rain pelted the sidewalk. The shop was a one hundred year old house that had been renovated into a cozy cafe.

In the front were antique couches and some throw blankets. It had a grand, hand-carved wooden fireplace, the old fashioned kind you don't see built anymore. An ornate hand chiseled design was carved into the antique wood. There was a case full of homemade cakes, and cupcakes with cream cheese icing sliding off their tops.

People sat around warming their hands on their cups, an chatter drifted along the old tin ceilings of each room. ordered four lattes at the counter, then sank into a velve couch, tucking my feet under me to wait for my children join me. I pushed a wisp of hair out of my eyes and held m shoulders back with ease as I gazed around the room. "Sile Night" played softly throughout the house. The notes mad the corners of my mouth turn up instantly with a smile, and felt a real sense of peace.

I thought about the Gardener, and how he caught ea flower petal in his garden. If those petals meant that much him, how much more valuable must be the Spirit of Wisdo that he given to me?

My children arrived and joined me in front of t fireplace. A young girl dropped off the coffees for us all at t same time, piping hot with perfect foam. I was trying to s the top off my latte, but it burned my lips, and my childr were making me laugh.

I set it down in front of me on a small coffee table. Th was the first time in years that I had sat down to talk with three of them together and I couldn't believe this day w happening.

At first it was awkward, and the conversation strained. I told them stories about when they were little and the funny things that happened. They, on the other hand, seemed to recall every embarrassing mishap I ever had as a parent.

My middle daughter became comfortable as the memories came flooding back, and it seemed like no time had passed at all. She let her walls down, and we were talking about life as if we had never left off.

The young girl who had made our lattes came by with a small clay pot. She set it on the coffee table before us and flipped her long bangs out of her eyes.

"Fresh baked today, compliments of the owner, Mr. Lamb! Merry Christmas!" she said with joy, as she bustled off to another room.

I tipped my head in curiosity as the aroma of the goodies hit my nose. Inside the small clay pot was finely twisted linen containing fresh baked bread. The inside was fluffy with a crusty, amber top.

There was a small tremble under the coffee table in front of us. We looked in surprise as the clay pot that held the bread began to shake. Then the pot broke, dividing in two.

We stared in silence for a moment at the pot. My oldest daughter peeked at the inside and the bread was also divided in two.

"Our Heavenly Father loves us. He broke the bread for us," she said gently. We each reached out and took a piece.

"This is the absolute best bread I've ever had!" said my middle daughter with her mouth full. "It's melting in my mouth like sugar!" My son reached into the clay pot for another piece.

"Mom, you gotta try this!" he exclaimed. As I put the bread in my mouth, the sweet, yet earthy taste was unmistakable, melting instantly on my tongue. It was something I had tasted only once before.

My body tingled all over again as the memory came immediately to my mind, and I smiled. Just as he said would.

Glancing at my children, a wonderful idea formed in my mind. I wanted more than anything for everyone to meet him face to face and it became very important to me.

I realized that we had been in the cafe a long time, but the conversation had come easily. Over the years time had crept on, and I wondered where time had gone as I looked into each of my children's faces with tenderness.

My middle daughter was very animated with her hands, telling a story about a prank her friends had tried to pull on her.

It had been so long since I had a relationship with her that I couldn't believe I was looking into her eyes like I was that day. Emotion started to rise in my heart, and I felt very blessed.

I looked down, and a tiny ant scurried across the coffee table in front of me. Maybe God takes the dead flowers in our hearts and waters them, so that some day they bloom again.

She paused and looked over at me with a huge grin.

I looked into each one of my children's faces.

"How do you all feel about taking a little trip to see a garden with me one day?" I asked them.

My middle daughters eyes lit up in surprise and then relaxed into a smile. "We would love that, mom…." she said quietly. Tears of joy welled up in the corners of my eyes, and I knew right then what really mattered.

My children began chattering again, and I sat back and folded my hands in my lap. I thought about my life and true acceptance. All along, the garden wasn't the answer I was looking for. All my life I had been searching through the flowers for peace, but my heart really longed for their creator. Finding him meant I never had to question his love for me. When he finally planted me, I knew that my name was written on the palm of his hand.

Chapter Six: A Gift of Grace

The butterfly finishes drinking the nectar and takes off through the air, swirling in the breeze as if being pulled by silky threads. Rather than flapping their wings like birds in an up and down manner, butterflies contract their bodies in order to make a slanted figure eight pattern using their wings. The air propels their contracted body through the air and shifts the butterfly along, as delicate as rice paper. This is how they seem to "float" through the air. They are able to see a wide range of ultraviolet colors that are invisible to our human eyes. Flowers also have ultraviolet markings that show the way to its nectar source. In this way, God designed a map system so the butterfly could always make it to the perfect flower! Then, the butterfly comes home…

"We are here!" I yelled fervently, as we hurried past the sign marking Grace's Garden. Droves of people were pouring into the garden. Today was the day! The enthusiasm in the air was palpable as people from all nations moved as one.

Every kind and color of people were present, and they were playing all kinds of instruments.

Notes of praise soared through the air in a choreographed song that sang of leading the way home. Banners were thrust high above the crowd, and the unseen currents rang out in freedom.

My arms interlocked with my children's as I led them up and down the familiar paths. As we passed by the greenhouse, my children spied the verdant glow of the green glass, so we stopped to peek inside. It was completely empty, and someone had clumsily nailed up a makeshift sign covering Mr. Lamb's that read, "Prince of the Garden". I saw the sign and shook my head.

Countless people, as many as the grains of sand on the seashore, were pouring into the garden. They caught us up a pulsating throng and carried us towards the inner court. Their emotion was spontaneous and bursting with joy!

Finally, we arrived at the middle, and standing there before the spring was the Lamb of God. Standing beside him was a glistening angel. The angel gripped a flaming sword, flashes of fire licking the shaft of the blade. He flashed it back and forth to guard the way. The Lamb of God stepped forward, radiantly shining in pure white from head to toe, as brilliant as the rays of the sun.

I looked closely at his face, and a smile formed at the corners of his mouth. The lines around his eyes and cheeks still drew a map in his crinkled skin, and I saw him just as he was. I knew he was the same today as he was yesterday. Struck with reverence, every person fell to the ground, their knees striking the soft grass.

The water from the spring slapped the banks high up over its rim like living water. It was now a river that we could not cross, because the water had risen and was deep enough to swim in. Now the Jordan is at flood stage all during harvest time, and it was deeper than before.

One by one, everyone gazed upon the water, wondering how we would reach the other side.

"You need a way to get across…" said a low, gravelly voice. There was the fox, poised and confident. He seemed larger than life, his orange red coat glistening in the light. He swaggered up to the people, grinning from ear to ear as if harboring a secret. He walked forward on his hind legs like a human. "Too bad this old man neglected to mention that you must be transformed in order to reach the Tree of Life," he breathed. Silence reigned as the fox's words settled upon the crowd.

He held up one of his nails, its sharp tip gleaming like dagger. He sadly observed the spring of water with its depth "You will all drown to death if you even attempt to cross th spring by yourselves," he observed. He glanced over at th Lamb of God who stood in the radiance of his glory, the exa representation of his nature. Indignation ignited in the corne of the fox's eyes and he carefully rearranged his features.

His eyes roamed across the myriads of people before hi with pity. "There is only one clear choice," he said, bold pronouncing each word. His eyes widened in anticipation.

"You can all simply stay here in the safety of the out court. I am prince of this garden, and I will shelter you. The will be peace and restoration here between you, and you w have no more need for this clown! There will be no mo tears; just love, pure love! With the love you show to ea other, you will all change each others hearts and live perfect peace!"

The fox's face glowed in the reflection of the water like angel of light. Some of the people crossed their arms a seemed confused. Others shifted their feet, and someo coughed. But no one moved.

With bristling fur, he jabbed his paw towards the rushing water. "You don't have a way! You aren't able to enter that holy place by yourselves!" he shrieked. "Do you really want to drown today by blindly following this so-called man?" Anger boiled in the pit of my stomach and without hesitation I thrust my finger at him.

"I know this fox, and he is a liar!" I screamed. "Only God can give us new hearts!"

The fox ignored me. He threw up his paws into the air, raw intensity exploding all over his face as he regarded the Lamb of God, pure hatred spewing out of the crevices of his features. He leaned in a little closer to the crowd of people, his brow skewed with anxiety.

"You can all rest in the garden with me! Isn't peace and restoration what you ultimately desire?" he asked. Every person stared at him. "You can't enter the inner court to the Holy of Holies and touch the Tree of Life, or YOU WILL ALL SURELY DIE!" Quiet filled the air, and the leaves above us gently waved back and forth in the soft breeze. The distinct sounding of a rooster suddenly blasted in the distance and every head turned towards the sound.

The Lamb of God stepped forward, stretching out his arms. He revealed the holes to everyone in each of his wrist where he had been pierced all the way through.

"I AM THE WAY, THE TRUTH AND THE LIFE! NO ONE COMES TO THE FATHER EXCEPT THROUGH ME!" he proclaimed.

At his mighty words, all the people fell immediately to the ground as though dead. His thunderous voice smashed into our faces, and the fox was knocked over onto his belly.

The ground beneath us trembled with a mighty roar, and everyone grabbed someone else in order to steady themselves. The fox's body writhed on the ground grotesquely squirming as he started to wriggle and change shape.

With guttural sounds, he began to mutate right in front our eyes. His orange red fir melted into the folds of his skin and a double coat of armor burst out in its place like popping rows of iron. His chest was as hard as a rock, the folds of his flesh tightly joined, firm and immovable. His legs retracted into his flesh. His bloodshot eyes slowly enlarged and snarled with an unfathomable noise. Flames were streaming from his mouth like sparks of fire shooting out.

Smoke poured from his nostrils, as from a boiling pot over burning reeds. His snorting threw out flashes of light, his eyes like the rays of dawn. He slowly glared up at the crowd, now a horror that slithers on the ground. Everyone exhaled in total shock as we saw the terrible creature that had transformed right before us. My middle daughter furrowed her brows, unfazed at the sight. She gazed at the hideous beast, and looked him up and down.

"Now wait just a minute, this thing creeps on the ground?" she said, her voice dripping with contempt. She glanced over at the Lamb of God who stood in radiant glory. "God gave us dominion over every creeping thing on earth!" she said pointedly. "So you Satan, can go to hell where you belong!" She put her hands on her hips. Then she turned and faced the crowd. With a high voice she declared, "We can enter the Holy place and take from the Tree of Life because *we are with God, and his spirit is within us*! We are the temple of the Lord! That is the only way, because God is the tree! *He is the way!*"

"NO!" Satan screamed, as he realized in horror what the Lamb of God was about to do.

A deafening silence fell upon the congregation. Satan squirmed on the grass, his chest heaving; the smoke from his nostrils burned with a stench that smelled like sulfur.

In one long sweep, the angel withdrew his flaming sword. The fire that licked the length of the blade cooled and disappeared as the Lamb of God began to move. The sound he made was like a gentle whisper as he reached the edge of the spring. As soon as he reached the waters edge, the water from upstream stopped flowing, and the waters were divided in two. It piled up in a heap at a great distance away. He stepped into the spring, and stopped in the middle of the Jordan and stood there on dry ground, shining as a brilliant light for all to see. For as the soil makes the sprout come up and a garden causes seeds to grow, so the Sovereign Lord will make righteousness and praise spring up before all nations.

When all the people of the earth saw the amazing thing that he had done, we knew that the living God was among us. In one voice, we shouted and sang with an ear-piercing noise. Satan slumped in defeat.

The angel stepped forward, striking out with his hand and gripping satan by his neck. With a mighty heave, catapulted him into the air, into the abyss.

We watched his body fly through the air until it was no longer visible, and everyone screamed with a deafening roar.

We hurried to cross over the Jordan, entering with thanksgiving and praise. The Lamb of God called us each by name, holding out his right arm to help each person pass and cross over onto dry ground.

He remained standing in the middle as streams of people reached the other side. Each one of us had the Spirit of Wisdom living inside us, enabling us to cross. We were a living temple of the Lord.

Finally, it was my turn to go. I was breathing deeply as I put one foot down onto the bottom of the spring. I felt the tingly feeling of the Holy Spirit flowing down through my body and knew he was with me. I stopped, looking up to see that he was firmly planted in the middle of the spring, his right arm outstretched to me. A huge smile radiated across his face.

"Well, I am waiting for you!" he laughed. I smiled to myself and carefully put another foot down onto the bottom of the spring. I began the short walk to the other side, my feet crunching on the dry rocky bed below. I reached out for his hand and he grabbed me, laughing with excitement.

He pulled me close in a warm hug, and I hurried across t
the other side. I reached the bank on the opposite shore, and
felt someone's hands grab me and help lift me up over th
embankment. I sobbed as my children cried out when the
also reached the shore.

I grabbed all my children in my arms and squeezed the
with all my might. My family, friends, and people I kne
were behind us also, looking for us.

My eyes welled up in tears. I was speechless, and I looke
back into my children's faces.

As the people streamed in more and more, the waters
the Jordan stayed open, and the nations walked by the ligh
The Lamb of God was now among us. We saw his face, ar
we didn't need the light of a lamp, or the light of the sun, f
he gave us light.

The Tree of Life was fully grown then, yielding fru
Each tiny moment of growth was evident in the lines of t
branches and fronds that now stretched up and reached out
far as the eye could see.

Its twisted boughs and massive roots sprawled over t
expanse of the island like a heavenly poem.

The wind picked up and blew gently, and a single leaf detached itself and slowly floated down to me. I reached out and caught it with my hand, my heart beating fast. I opened my hand to look at the leaf, and my name was on it in large bold print. The letters were etched out in the veins of the leaf across its blade. I cried out in surprise and looked up at my children who were smiling. They caught my arm and said, "We love you, mom." I looked and saw that they were each holding a leaf of their own. As I looked around, I saw all the people grasping hands and laughing with excitement, their leaves in their hands.

I had become unshakable in my faith even though some branches of my story had been pruned along the way. All along, God knew what was best for us without having to say too many words. There had been steps along the way where there had been uncertainty and doubt, but once I met him and placed my trust in him, all those feelings completely disappeared.

Knowing I was living in perfect love with him meant that I wasn't afraid for him to see inside me.

Loss comes to everyone on earth at some point in time. once had a hole in my heart so deep, that I never imagine that I would find love again. God restores us by filling th hole with his grace, breaking us of everything we place abov him, so that instead of drowning, he can lead us to di ground.

In his mercy, he makes us wait for his timing, because h changes our hearts without it being in our own human effo This demonstrates his sovereign nature and expels our egos.

Just like a sword is sharp without help, we can all live changed life through the power of the Holy Spirit, instead being desperate to make people see we have done things prove ourselves to mankind.

For the word of God is alive and active. Sharper than a double-edged sword, it penetrates even to dividing soul a spirit, joints and marrow; it judges the thoughts and attitud of the heart. Nothing in all creation is hidden from Goc sight. Everything is uncovered and laid bare before the ey of him whom we must give account.

I wasn't afraid to let him see the truth, the real me that no one else can see. I could be myself.

I wasn't terrified of his judgement because my sins were wrapped up in the form of the two nail holes he showed me that pierced his wrists. He had already judged my sins at the cross. This is what it meant to live in freedom. I believed in him and had been set free. So to him, each one of us had been washed as pure as the blood he shed for us on the cross. *A gift of grace.*

Meet the author:

Noelle Sellers lives in Atlanta Georgia with her dog Bailey. She has three children and enjoys painting and nature. This is her first writing endeavor.

Made in the USA
Columbia, SC
28 October 2020